NOT TO SCALE.

FOR IDENTIFICATION

PURPOSES ONLY.

THE MALT-STARS OF WARMINSTER

The Remarkable Survival of Britain's Oldest Working Maltings

ROBIN APPEL

First published in 2010
Copyright © Warminster Maltings Ltd.

Publisher: Warminster Maltings Ltd.
Design and production: Cradduck Design Co. Ltd. www.cradduck.com
Prepress and print: Culverlands Press Ltd.

Telephone: +44 (0) 1985 212014
Email: chris.garratt@warminster-malt.co.uk
Web: www.warminster-malt.co.uk

ISBN: 978-0-9566498-0-5

The Malt-stars of Warminster

The Remarkable Survival of
Britain's Oldest Working Maltings

THE COUNTRYSIDE RESTORATION TRUST

The Countryside Restoration Trust was established in 1993 by the Chairman, Robin Page, the late Sir Laurens van der Post and the late artist and conservationist, Gordon Beningfield. The Trust is a farming and conservation charity which aims to protect and restore Britain's countryside with wildlife-friendly and commercially-viable agriculture. It is committed to promoting the importance of a living and working countryside through education, demonstration and community involvement.

The Trust is also establishing a network of demonstration farms across Britain which, using sensitive farming methods, will show how to protect wildlife, produce quality, seasonal food and preserve our countryside for future generations.

It is also using these living, working farms as educational centres of expertise to inspire farmers, land managers, the general public and politicians.

For all these reasons all proceeds from the sale of this book have been granted to the Trust.

The Countryside Restoration Trust
Haslingfield Road
Barton
Cambridge
CB23 7AG

Tel: 01223 262999
E-mail: info@livingcountryside.org.uk
www.livingcountryside.org.uk

Charity Reg No. 1007793

Dedicated to the Malt-stars of Warminster, both former and present, and to the townspeople of Warminster for their long-standing and undying support.

FOREWORD

The British are notoriously bad at celebrating the things we do well. You would never know, from reading the public prints, that Britain remains not only a great beer-drinking nation but also that the country is witnessing an astonishing revival of the brewing art. There are now more than 700 breweries in Britain, twice the number than when the Campaign for Real Ale was launched in the early 1970's. The revival is accompanied by a great fascination with beer styles among craft brewers. As a result, pubs no longer offer just mild and bitter with a winter warmer for Christmas. Discerning drinkers can now find true India Pale Ales, brewed to Victorian recipes, porters, stouts, old ales and barley wines.

But the industry is not stuck in the past. The popularity of such "new age" beers as golden ale is the result of the determination of the new breed of craft brewers to offer a wide range of beers in an attempt to win younger drinkers to the joys of cask ale. Along with the regard for beer style, there is also great interest among both brewers and drinkers with the raw materials used in the brewing process. For a decade or more, thanks to the vigorous work of farmers, we are all more "hop savvy" and can talk with considerable knowledge about the different characteristics of a Fuggle and a Golding, a Cascade and a Willamette. Barley has tended to sit in the shadow of the hop plant but now, thanks to the passion and dedication of maltsters such as Robin Appel, it's emerging into the limelight and taking centre stage.

Older brewers call barley "the soul of beer". In the thirty years or more I have been writing about beer, I have never ceased to marvel at both the importance of barley to brewing and the astonishing way in which the grain is subtly transformed to provide the essential sugars for fermentation. At its simplest, wine can be made by crushing grapes and allowing the natural yeasts on the skins to start fermentation. If you crush an ear of barley, on the other hand, nothing happens. It takes the great skill of maltsters to steep raw grain and kiln it in order for beer-making to take place.

As this book shows, malting has declined alarmingly over the past one hundred years. I live in Hertfordshire and I'm saddened when I drive through Ware to see that all the great maltings in the town are either derelict or have been turned into private dwellings or offices. The fact that Warminster is alive and thriving is a cause for celebration. But Warminster goes beyond mere celebration. Its management has a very modern outlook, one that meets with the demands of consumers to know what goes into their food and drink.

One of the first things I learnt when I started out as a beer writer was that craft brewers considered Maris Otter to be – far and away – the finest malting barley. It's a variety that delivers a rich biscuity character and flavour to beer and it also works in harmony with brewer's yeast. I recall vividly the revered head brewer of a renowned regional company telling me that, on instructions from the dreaded accountants, he had switched to a cheaper "high yielding" strain of barley. As a result, he found that his yeast sulked in the fermenter and refused to work the usual magic of converting malt sugars into alcohol. He returned, swiftly and happily, to Maris Otter.

Craft brewers are busily restoring some of the beer styles that made Britain famous throughout the world. They have been joined in this enterprise by Robin Appel, his associates and dedicated farmers, who produce malting barley of the finest quality. And the malt can be traced back to its fields of origin. Cynics will no doubt laugh at the fact that craft brewers can say they prefer Farmer Giles's version of Maris Otter to the grain from Farmer Silas's neighbouring fields. But Warminster's Warranty of Origin will both please discerning drinkers and help place beer in the twenty-first century on a par with the finest wines.

The underlying theme of this splendid book is "small is beautiful". Malt and beer can be made in vast, soulless factories. But hand-crafted beer needs malt made with similar dedication. Warminster may be based in Victorian buildings but it looks to a future where integrity in food production will be seen as ever more important. This is a book dedicated to tradition, to quality and, above all, to the amazing flowering of good British beer.

Roger Protz

Roger Protz edits the CAMRA Good Beer Guide.
His website can be found at www.beer-pages.com

PREFACE

When I first set out to try and buy Warminster Maltings, back in 1999, as far as I was concerned I was just buying a business, a small traditional 'floor' maltings. Despite its size, I felt confident it could turn a profit by targeting its malt sales exclusively at the new generation of micro-breweries establishing themselves right across the country. Included in my calculations was my responsibility for maintaining the much revered malting barley variety Maris Otter, and it seemed to me that this barley combined with the traditional floor process of malting, ought to deliver a superior malt which many craft brewers would be keen to buy into.

When in 2001 I finally took ownership of the business, I was only vaguely aware of the maltings' heritage, and I had no idea of the amount of archive material that had been retained, and the amount that could be uncovered once I started to look for it. Over the next two years, as I sifted through the many envelopes stuffed full of documents and correspondence, I began to get a picture of a remarkable story of survival against the odds, quite apart from an increased impression of the significance of Dr Beaven. During their stewardship, different managers had compiled manuscripts describing 'the process of malting' and 'malting at Warminster', and a set of black and white photographs recorded each procedure that was the malting process at Pound Street in 1950. For all of this I am very grateful, but what soon became very apparent to me was that what was really needed was for all this information to be strung together.

So here was a book that needed to be written, and although I have been the person best placed to do this, my literary talents do not qualify me as the perfect choice, but I have done my best. In this, I am much indebted to Jennifer Doney, who converted my original longhand manuscript to electronic, to Carol Purdue, who persevered with all the corrections and alterations, and marshalled all the illustrations, to Sandra Bates for her painstaking research in the County Records Office, and to John Somers for all his patience over many weeks as together we turned the sheaf of pages into a book.

What follows is a compilation of everything at my disposal, a brief story of what is widely regarded not only as Britain's oldest working maltings, but also one of this country's richest brewing heritage sites.

Robin Appel,
The Malt House, Droxford.

11th August 2010

List of Colour Plates

Contents

Chapter 1

Introduction

Warminster Maltings, Pound Street elevation, by Dorset artist Bill Toop R1.

The story of Warminster Maltings and its survival is remarkable. It was built more than 150 years ago just as all the neighbouring malthouses across this Wiltshire market town were closing. One hundred years ago it was an unlikely academy for one of the UK's greatest agricultural pioneers, and, on the scale of malt production common across the industry by the 1960's it was an extremely unlikely survivor when most of Britain's traditional 'floor' maltings were judged to be no longer economical, and were shut. But survive it has done and the common thread to its longevity has been, and continues to be, its succession of proprietors, who significantly, have all been very active within and benefited from industry directly related to malt.

Back in the 18th Century there were up to 36 malthouses in Warminster, and it was said between them they generated a malt trade that was bigger than any other town in the West of England. Bristol and much of Somerset was supplied with malt from the town's malthouses, and such was the reputation of the malt produced that across the county of Somerset many inns displayed a sign "Warminster Malt", to emphasise the superior quality of their ales.

This industry was a natural development from the agriculture which surrounded the town, derived from the vast areas of chalk downland that is Salisbury Plain, the perfect soil type for the production of barley. As a result throughout the 18th and early 19th century Warminster was an important corn market - farmers, merchants and maltsters met once a week on Saturdays when ample supplies of premium quality barley were scrutinised and traded. Members of some of the principal families of Warminster, such as the Aldridges, Bucklers, Slades and Wanseys were all maltsters, but by the early 19th century the trade somewhat declined, albeit it was still described as considerable.

Throughout the 19th century malt production in Warminster followed a natural progression, falling into fewer hands as the more successful maltsters expanded and the rest quietly closed. By the second half of the century the number of firms engaged in malting was no more than six, and twenty years later it was only two.

There is every indication that the Warminster Maltings Pound Street site, which was remodelled in 1879, is a direct result if not a direct cause of the decline of the other firms. As malthouses around the town were demolished, it would appear construction materials were salvaged and taken to Pound Street evidenced by the design and construction of each of the malt floors, which internally are all somewhat different. The architect of this design was William Morgan whose family had not only been brewers but also maltsters in the town from as early as 1822. William Morgan handed the business on to his son, William Frank Morgan, who continued to run the maltings until shortly before his death in 1907. To this day Morgan junior's name remains etched above the west door "William Frank Morgan, Licensed Maltster".

But prior to his death, in 1902 William Frank Morgan transferred the business to his much younger brother-in-law Edwin Sloper Beaven who had joined him in 1878 following a brief career on the Beaven family farm at nearby Heytesbury. It was Beaven, perhaps unwittingly, who was to seal the future of the maltings through his collaboration with the Guinness company. Initially this came about from his interest in barley breeding and his liaison with the Guinness Research Laboratory in Dublin over matters of experimental design and measurement with regard to the hybridisation of barley varieties. This led to malt production contracts with Guinness, and later on, as Beaven became more absorbed in his barley breeding, he turned over the whole of his malt production exclusively for Guinness, supplying both Dublin and the new Park Royal brewery in London.

As if traditional 'floor' maltings did not face a big enough challenge throughout the 20th century from new technology, they were also always at risk of their own self destruction – from fire. The management of coal fired kilns, and hot dry malt within part timber structures was always potentially dangerous, and malthouses were regularly gutted by fire, and sometimes completely destroyed, even within months of being built. Pound Street was lucky, the fire

DISASTROUS FIRE AT WARMINSTER FACTORY

Bath and Wilts Chronicle, Thursday, November 6th 1924.

in 1924 (November 5th perchance!) that completely destroyed the barley store, above the steeps, was mostly contained at that end of the complex. Beaven rebuilt and repaired all the damage.

When Beaven died in 1941, the business comprised of offices in East Street and two malting sites in Warminster: Pound Street and Market Place; and the Montpelier Maltings in Bristol. His trustees continued the business until 1947 when a new company was formed, E S Beaven (Maltings) Ltd, a wholly owned subsidiary of Arthur Guinness Son & Co Ltd.

Beaven's daughter, Miss Alice Beaven, was appointed a director of the new company, and two more maltings at Diss and Gt Yarmouth in Norfolk were added to the portfolio, all administered from the East Street offices in Warminster. There then followed nearly 50 years of well resourced, stable production at Pound Street all underwritten by the global expansion of Guinness stout.

In 1968 the Market Place Maltings, a unique 'one man' malthouse, was closed when the operator finally retired (the building is still easily identified in Chinns Walk today). Then in 1970 Miss Alice Beaven died, and the following year the Montpelier Maltings, being in a poor state of repair, was also closed. However, throughout the whole of the Guinness era, the freehold of the Pound Street Maltings remained firmly in the hands of the Beaven family. This was probably because Guinness always envisaged building a modern malting plant on land adjacent to their Barley Research Farm to the east of the town, close to the village of Codford. A new road access, directly off the A36 (still visible today) was constructed in order to 'lock in' the planning permission which had been granted, but that was as far as the new plan ever progressed.

The Warminster Maltings Guinness did close – the one-man malthouse in Chinns Court, as seen today.

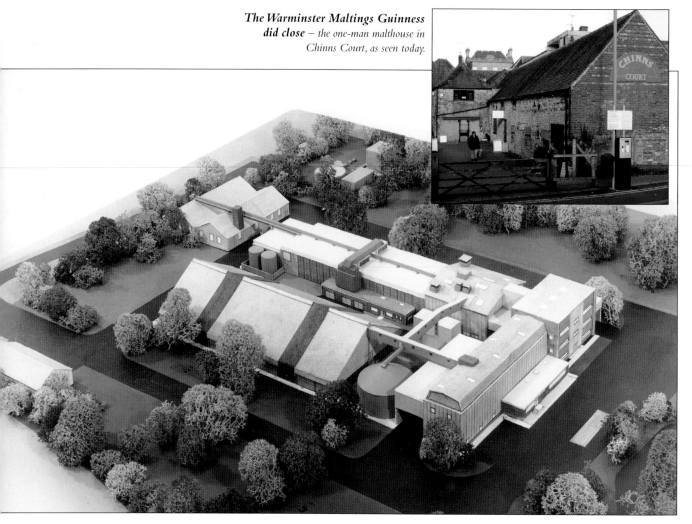

The Warminster Maltings Guinness never opened – architect's model of the new plant to be built at Codford.

Guinness Malt-stars 1986. David Miles (first left), Chris Garratt (fourth left), Lawrence Hampton (third right) and Hugh Turner (second right) were all pivotal to the survival of Warminster Maltings.

Then in 1994, the announcement everyone at Warminster had been predicting for so long, was eventually delivered. The Warminster Journal, 20th May 1994, carried the front page headline "Guiness Pull the Plug: Maltings to Close". Having, in theory, achieved a stay of execution for just on 30 years, finally it seemed the game was up. But one of the ten men about to receive their redundancy cheques had other ideas.

In 1976, Chris Garratt had been interviewed for his position at Beaven's still in his school uniform. It was his first job and he had become so wedded to it he was not prepared to give up just yet.

To get him started he was able to negotiate a modest supply contract to Guinness, buying time for him to present himself to brewers in the region, and restart the original business of 'sales maltster' abandoned by Beaven nearly 80 years before. But the private backing Garratt had secured for this project eventually proved inadequate and he needed someone with much more commitment to support him if he was to go on.

"Appel identified a synergy between the Maltings, Maris Otter and the renaissance of the brewing industry."

In 2001, Robin Appel, the Hampshire based barley merchant whose name is synonymous with the much revered barley variety 'Maris Otter', stepped in and purchased the business, "lock, stock and barrel". Appel identified a synergy between the Maltings, 'Maris Otter' and the renaissance of the brewing industry in the form of micro-breweries which seemed to be opening everywhere. Warminster Maltings size, by now almost unique on the scale of malting production in the UK, was much better suited to serving these small scale breweries. Appel considered the Pound Street site worth saving for this reason alone. For by now, Warminster Maltings was one of only six floor maltings left still serving the brewing industry, (shortly to be one of four just 3 years later). Of these, only two (Warminster and Newton Abbott) retain their architectural integrity, and besides this, Warminster boasts a heritage that arguably makes it the most famous maltings in the world!

Chapter 2

WILLIAM FRANK MORGAN – LICENSED MALTSTER

William Frank Morgan

R ecords are sketchy, but William Frank Morgan appears to have been at least a third generation maltster following his father, William Morgan, who, in turn, succeeded his uncle who was a practising maltster in East Street, Warminster, as early as 1822. William Morgan preceded his son in the Pound Street malthouses, and it was he who was responsible for their early construction. Up until 1854 the Pound Street site was registered as a "House, Outbuildings and Garden", the property of John Bleeck, a wool broker. However, on the 30th September of that same year, the property described as "late in the tenure or occupancy of John Bleeck (deceased) now void" was conveyed by indenture to "William Morgan, Common Brewer".

There is little dispute that the construction of the main complex took place in two stages, the northern half (floors 1 & 2 plus adjoining buildings) about ten years before the southern half (floors 3 & 4 plus adjoining buildings). In fact Kiln No. 1 (northern half) has two walls facing onto the floors which predate the rest of the construction, and are almost certainly part of the original house.

By 1865 a town plan shows the site is fronted by two adjoining non-residential buildings. i.e. completion of the project! The join between the buildings is clearly marked, and confirmed in the 1871 census as numbers 21 and 22 Pound Street. From this we can deduce that William Morgan purchased the site for the purpose of building a new maltings, and got on with it straight away, and may well have been up and running with 'Stage One' of the project in time for the 1855 harvest. Miss Alice Beaven, daughter of E S Beaven, and grand daughter of William Morgan would have known exactly – in 1958 she referred to "our Grandfathers old malthouses here are still in use".

But it is William Frank Morgan who is credited with the re-modelling of the Pound Street complex in 1879. What exactly that involved is difficult to determine, because one outstanding feature of the construction is that no single pair of malt floors (i.e. upper and lower levels) has common construction materials at the ground floor level. For example, Number 1 (lower) has a timbered ceiling, it is the only floor that has. Whether this was all William Morgan's doing, or the outcome of the intervention of William Frank Morgan in 1879, we do not know, but the variety of design may well have been the result of salvaging building materials from demised malthouses in the town. William Frank Morgan's reason for remodelling after only 24 years is not recorded either but we can imagine it might have been to boost production, or to benefit from the now scaled down regulations of the Malt Tax, or both.

The design for the whole complex is described as of the Ware pattern - Ware in Hertfordshire, at the time, one of the most mature malting centres in England. At one end is a first floor barley store, with steeping cisterns set below. The main trunk of the building comprises the working floors, one laid above the other, and replicated four times across the complex. The outer walls feature regular small windows along their length, windows which are non-glazed, but shuttered for ventilation control.

The working floors lead to what is always the outstanding feature of most maltings, the kiln. At Warminster, there were originally four kilns, one for each pair of floors. At least two of these

"Two adjoining non-residential buildings." Pound Street frontage today.

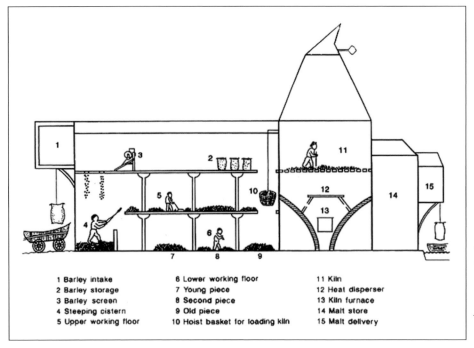

1 Barley intake
2 Barley storage
3 Barley screen
4 Steeping cistern
5 Upper working floor

6 Lower working floor
7 Young piece
8 Second piece
9 Old piece
10 Hoist basket for loading kiln

11 Kiln
12 Heat disperser
13 Kiln furnace
14 Malt store
15 Malt delivery

A typical early nineteenth century two-floor malting.

Source:
J. Brown, 'Steeped in Tradition' p. 52.

kilns (Kilns No. 1 and No. 2) were pyramid shaped, and were of timber and plaster construction covered with slate, topped with a flat mushroom cap. Today, only Kiln No. 1 remains, having been restored and fitted with a louvred pagoda cap. Finally, and adjacent to the kilns, are the malt stores which front the complex along Pound Street, convenient for loading the malt onto horse drawn wagons.

A typical late 19th century feature at Warminster is the addition of an extra kiln for drying barley, built in red brick, immediately adjacent to the barley intake.

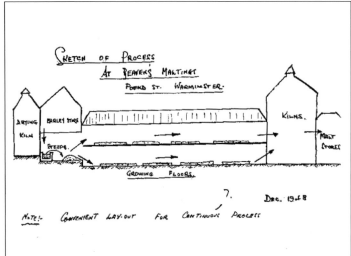

Sketch of Beaven's Maltings, Pound Street, Warminster, Dec. 1948.

The Maltings today.

Much of the construction of the maltings is of stone, typical of the early 19th century, and no doubt in the belief it protected internal temperature from greater fluctuation. Continuing this theme, and again typically of the early 19th century, the buildings could be described as squat, but for very good reason. Firstly, the lower working floors are set below ground level to help reduce the temperature over the floors in the warmer weather. Secondly, the ceilings of the working floors are very low, less than 6 feet, in order to maintain a greater constancy of temperature across the floor when malting is in progress.

Finally, and another classic feature of the maltings, is the central courtyard which is not parallel sided as it first appears, but deliberately gently wedge shaped, to enhance ventilation to the lower floor windows. This feature is replicated at 19th century malting sites right across the country, and further adds to the importance of Warminster Maltings as typical of the period.

The design of the maltings complex pre-determines a 'flow diagram' that is the traditional process of malting.

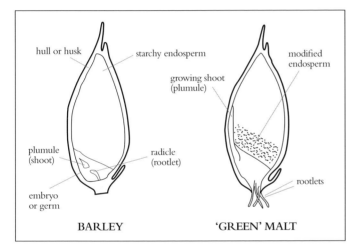

The germination of barley.

Malt is grain, mostly barley, which has been germinated artificially, when enzymes convert the starch in the grain into a sugar called maltose. When the conversion process is complete, it is arrested, by drying the 'green' malt in a kiln, to conserve the sugar for further processing when it can be, for example, fermented with yeast for brewing, providing not just the alcohol, but also the flavour and colour of beer.

One hundred years ago the malting process at Pound Street took up to three weeks, and began by first cleaning the barley over slotted screens in the barley store. Then the barley was dropped into a cistern for steeping the grain in fresh water for three to four days in order to raise the moisture content and induce germination. The drained barley was then shovelled out of the cistern into a heap known as a 'couch' where it sat for a further 24 hours for it to swell and warm up, prior to being spread, by hand shovels, onto the germinating floors.

On the floors, which form the main body of a traditional maltings, the barley was spread to an even depth of between 3 to 12 inches (7 to 30cm) depending on the ambient temperature, for about 12 to 15 days. The illustration on page 10 pictures the process known as the 'piece method' whereby 3 or 4 batches of 'green' malt were systematically moved along the floor from the steep to the kiln. Latterly, bigger batches and the 'strip method' have been adopted whereby one batch stretches along the full length of the floor. The barley was regularly turned, by hand, so that it was uniformly exposed to the air, and development of the roots and shoots was strictly controlled. The shuttered windows, at regular intervals along the floors, were used to influence the temperature and humidity of the growing barley. When the head maltster deemed that the conversion of starch to sugar had been completed, the 'green' malt was swiftly transferred onto the coal fired kiln for drying over approximately 72 hours, when the length of time, temperature and draught were adjusted to impart different degrees of colour and flavour to the finished malt.

The final part of the process took place in the malt store when the malted grain was 'screened' to separate it from the dried shoots, known as malt culms, and the malt was then drawn into 4 bushel hessian sacks (100 kgs) ready for distribution to the breweries.

In 1855 the process of malting, and critically the design of Morgan's malthouses, was subject to the strict regulations based around the Malt Tax. A duty on malt was first imposed in 1644 to meet the growing costs of the Civil War, and over the next 200 years the inelastic demand for beer made this tax a 'soft' target for revenue generated in times of need. In fact, right up to its repeal in the late 19th century, it constantly generated in order of 10% of total income from taxation. However, by the end of the 18th century, the consequence of this enormous dependence on the one tax unleashed a complex web of legislation to prevent fraud and evasion.

Firstly, all maltsters had to be licensed – over the west door facing Pound Street is inscribed 'William Frank Morgan, Licensed Maltster'. The licence fee was pro-rata to the annual potential production of malt and the granting of a licence gave rise to constant inspection of the premises, and the process, to which excise officers had right of access at all times.

Maltsters then had to comply with a maze of rules and regulations covering every aspect of production, from the design, construction and positioning of the steeping cisterns, to the number of germinating floors, as well as the book keeping of barley and malt stocks. For example, the Pound Street Maltings have brick built, flat bottomed steeping cisterns, so designed so that the excise officers, using hand held measuring rods, could accurately measure the volumes of barley within the steeps. Then, there had to be a floor space between the steeping cisterns and the germinating floors, known as the 'couch'. This was where the freshly wetted barley was transferred from the steeps to warm up, and once again measured by the excise officers, before being spread across the germinating floors.

Before each batch of barley could be made into malt at Pound Street, written notice had to be sent to the excise office in the town 24 hours before the exact time of starting a fresh steep, stating the duration of the steeping process, and the exact quantity of grain involved.

The Malt Tax was charged at a flat rate on each bushel of grain processed to malt, with the volume gauged by the excise officer no less than three times: firstly, after 40 hours in the steep, secondly after 26 hours in the 'couch' and finally after 72 hours on the germinating floor. Tolerances were imposed for expansion of the grain throughout the process – 17.5% expansion in the 'couch', 33% expansion on the floors after exactly 72 hours, or up to 50% expansion thereafter.

Penalties were imposed for each breach of the regulations, of which there were fourteen for the steeping process alone, ten of which carried a £100 fine and four a £200 fine. The culmination of all these regulations was the 1827 Act, listing a total of 101 penalties, and fines totalling £13,500, should any maltster be unfortunate enough to be in breach of them all!

Universally, maltsters struggled with this burden of regulation, as almost certainly did the excise officers, often leading to punitive interpretation. Not surprisingly the 1827 Act was the final straw, as they say, and within months 1800 maltsters nationwide combined under a new Association of Maltsters of the United Kingdom to combat and argue for repeal of much of the legislation. But it was to be a long fought battle, and even eighteen years later 179 maltsters from what is commonly termed the region of Wessex, including William Morgan of Warminster, felt strongly enough to draw up a petition "agreed at Weyhill Fair, in the county of Hants, the 13th and 14th October 1845" and addressed to The Commissioners of Excise, expressing their grievance over the measuring of the expansion of the grain following steeping. They complained that fair trading was being harassed with "a vigour beyond the law" which created "an apparent delinquency, where none, by a fair procedure, would be found to exist".

However, by the late 1840's, the Association of Maltsters had for the most part succeeded, and much of the legislation had been repealed, and as for that which remained, common sense

Extract from "The Memorial of ... Maltsters, and Brewers (being also maltsters) agreed to at Weyhill Fair, in the county of Hants, the 13th and 14th October 1845."

appeared to prevail. So much so, and despite the long years of protest, when the Association of Maltsters eventually called for a replacement of the Malt Tax, the industry was opposed. The perceived difficulties of the legislation bound up with the tax had, there is no doubt, acted as a barrier to entry into the industry, and no-one within wanted to threaten that comfortable position. But in 1880, the Malt Tax was finally repealed, and replaced with a tax on beer. Unfortunately for William Frank Morgan, who at all times had meticulously respected the regulations imposed by the Malt Tax, and had re-modelled his maltings accordingly, this was just one year after the completion of all the work carried out to his Pound Street malthouse.

"Frank William Morgan delivered a long record of philanthropy."

That this newly revised malting complex was a success, there is no doubt, because by the time he died in 1907, William Frank Morgan had delivered a long record of philanthropy towards the town of Warminster. Besides the maltings, the Morgan family had also benefited from brewing interests in the town from around 1830, including The Warminster Brewery (1877–1904), a natural progression from their malting business. All this underlined W F Morgan's standing in the town, not only as a JP, but also, like his father before him, as the long standing chairman of the Local Board of Health. In 1894, following the Local Government Act of that year, the Board of Health was dissolved and the first Warminster Urban District Council was elected with Morgan as its chairman, a chair he held until 1904. In his last year of office, perhaps anticipating his retirement, Morgan's final gesture to the town was an offer to build a "municipal chamber" as a home for the UDC. He offered £400 to build what fellow councillors saw as his own personal memorial, which triggered a revolt on the council and Morgan was deposed. But the council still accepted his £400 which was redirected to the Fire Brigade Committee who were now able to build a new, much grander, fire station.

So the lasting memorial to William Frank Morgan is after all that corner of Pound Street Maltings, where his name remains etched above the west door. In 1904 he could never have imagined that his malthouses would have had the same impact and durability as that of a grand "municipal chamber". Nor is it likely at that stage that he could have foreseen the enormous impression that his immediate successor at the Pound Street Maltings was about to make upon the world and all which that entailed.

In 1902 Morgan had handed over his malting business to a much younger member of the family, his brother-in-law Edwin Sloper Beaven!

Warminster Fire Station

Chapter 3
EDWIN SLOPER BEAVEN 1857 – 1941

Dr. Edwin Sloper Beaven

The second of four children, Edwin Sloper Beaven was born in 1857 on his father's farm at Heytesbury, 4 miles from Warminster. Educated locally to begin with, at the age of 10 he went away to Framlingham College in Suffolk, where 3 years later in 1870 he passed the Junior Cambridge Local exam with honours. In doing so, he acquired a basic knowledge of chemistry which was to prove of enduring interest and value throughout his life. Aged just 13, he left school, imbibed with a desire to find out things for himself. From then onwards, he, in his own words "taught myself".

Beaven's family by now had moved to a 1,000 acre farm at Boreham, on the edge of Warminster, but shortly after his return home his father died and Beaven and his older brother helped their mother to carry on. However, eight years later, in 1878, the farm was given up and Beaven, who had by now acquired a good deal of farming knowledge, accepted an invitation from W F Morgan to join him in his malting business in Warminster. Then three years later he became a member of the Morgan family when he married his boss's youngest sister Margaret Fookes Morgan in 1881.

In those days making malt was a much more seasonal business, busy from October to May when malting had to stop as the daytime temperatures began to rise. This dovetailed neatly with the demand for labour on the land, when haymaking and harvesting the corn required many extra hands on farms, who then returned to the maltings in the autumn. The summer months were therefore able to afford Beaven ample time to slake his thirst for knowledge of agricultural matters by reading and experiment.

Besides this, there is every evidence that Beaven's boss, W F Morgan, as well as being an astute businessman, was a keen judge of barley and accomplished in all the skills required to produce best quality malt. In Morgan, Beaven probably had one of the best tutors to be found in the malting industry.

Working alongside Morgan, Beaven very quickly discovered that one of the first challenges to face maltsters was purchasing the barley, identifying principally by eye the right quality of barley that would in turn translate into quality malt. Barley was purchased direct from farmers who brought their grain into the town on market days. In 1878 market day was Saturday in Warminster and is best described in Beaven's own words, taken from his book *"Barley - Fifty Years of Observation and Experiment"*.

"The Market Place (at Warminster) was the main street of the town, along which every Saturday, in the open air and in all weathers, stood sacks of grain in a double row, as had been the custom for hundreds of years. All the grain to be sold was brought in on farmers' wagons and put into one or other of the stores, which were at that time attached to each of six or seven inns in the Market Place. The 'Bailiff' of the market took from the store one sack from each bulk, dipped out a quarter of a peck into a brass bowl, as was the customary right of the lord of the manor, and then set down the same sack on some wheat straw previously laid down for 'bedding' by the carters, whose perquisite it was to bring in as much of the farmers' straw on top of their loads as was necessary for this purpose and subsequently to sell the same.

Beaven's book, published posthumously in 1947.

Then on Saturday mornings dealings went on from about eleven to one o'clock, when all the farmers sat down to dinner at the 'ordinary', a function now, alas, in so many old market towns sadly depleted.

The chairmanship of each 'market ordinary' was a coveted office and the discussions over the gin-and-water which followed in the afternoons laid the foundation for all the Chambers of Agriculture and Farmers' Unions which were established later. But the farmer did not pay for the gin-and-water. Before that stage was reached the local millers, maltsters and corn chandlers, if they had not dined with the farmers, came in with banknotes stuffed into their top hats to pay for what they had bought. They already had inspected, if they so wished, the bulks of grain where they were stored, so there was no disputes as to whether the bulk was inferior to the 'market sack'; there were no guarantees about artificial drying; no arbitrations; no allowances!

Market Place, Warminster, 1880 with the market in progress. William Cobbett's opinion in 1826 in his 'Rural Rides' states "Warminster is a very nice town; everything belonging to it is solid and good."

But to revert to the gin-and-water. When the amount due was agreed, the buyer deducted sixpence for every ten quarters of grain he had paid for and this was spent there and then. Such were the good old times."

Selecting only the most suitable barleys for malting at Warminster's market was not a task for the inexperienced eye, and early in Beaven's malting career, the involved question of quality attracted his enquiring mind. His thoughts had been further ignited by the publication in 1882 of the book "Die Saatgerste" (the Act of Growing Barley) by the German scientist Friedrich Kornicke. Correspondence with Kornicke aroused Beaven's interest in the possibility of improving the then existing races of barley grown in the UK.

At the end of the 19th century the British barley crop was a complex patchwork of regional derivations of named barleys selected principally by farmers from the landrace varieties. For example, a named barley grown in Dorset could be markedly different from the same named barley grown in Berkshire. So when maltsters needed to widen their area of procurement due perhaps to an indifferent local harvest, they might find that a particular barley, with which they thought they were familiar, would prove to be somewhat different to that they expected. In those days buying malting barley required a very special skill.

In the 1870's the malting barley most commonly grown across Britain was a barley called 'Chevalier' a race of barley accidentally discovered by a farm worker John Andrews at Debenham, in Suffolk. This barley was multiplied by Andrews' landlord, the Rev J B Chevallier, after whom it was named (an 'l' however, being dropped during the process). The barley grains were of excellent malting quality but the straw was weak and became very brittle immediately prior to harvest when the ears of grain could break off, in a heavy down pour say, and be lost.

There were however, as already pointed out, numerous other barleys and derivations of barleys in cultivation across the regions. Prominent among these was 'Archer', an old English barley of unknown origin, better yielding than 'Chevalier' but of lower malting quality. There was also 'Spratt', less widely grown but with very stiff straw so it would remain standing to harvest where other barleys would not. Then there was 'Goldthorpe' raised from a single ear found in a field of 'Chevalier' barley by Mr Dyson of Goldthorpe, Yorks in 1889. 'Goldthorpe' was a considerable improvement on the aforementioned barleys and the fact of its discovery and its spread made a deep impression on Beaven.

So Beaven began a series of nursery and field experiments, firstly in the garden of his residence, and then from 1895 onwards on a more extended scale on a piece of land (4 acres) off Boreham Road, Warminster, which became known as the Boreham Road Barley Field. His objective was to discover and stabilize improved malting and brewing characteristics in barley combined with enhanced agronomic performance.

When, in 1895, Beaven took his two elder daughters to school in Bonn, he visited Kornicke, and was shown his barley cultivations in the Botanical Gardens of Poppelsdorf. Shortly afterwards Kornicke presented Beaven with an ear of each of the races of barley described in "Die Saatgerste". These were to be the foundation of a world collection of varieties of barley, compiled and studied by Beaven, from which he was to make his selections another day. To complete this collection Beaven made contact with the Foreign Office to ask them to arrange for all British Consular officials serving overseas, to send him samples of local barley. It is not known how many bureaucrats complied with the request, but in time the collection became an authoritative classification of the genus, published by Beaven in 1906, and

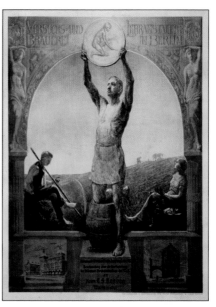

which remains a standard exposition of the subject. This work first brought Beaven to international prominence, for example, recognised in 1908 when the Brewing Research Institute of Berlin awarded him a silver commemorative medal.

Back in 1901 the Guinness Research Laboratory had been founded in Ireland, with Horace T Brown as its Director, and in the same year an experimental maltings was built in Dublin. Guinness were preparing for a thorough programme of investigation in to barley – what varieties to sow, how to grow them, and how to malt them. Beaven was already in correspondence with Dr Brown, and through him a life long association with Arthur Guinness Son & Co Ltd began, so that by 1904, Beaven turned over his malt production to exclusively 'commission malting' for the Dublin brewer. Beaven also became responsible for arranging the firm's supplies of imported barley from all parts of the world, no doubt with the help from his network of contacts in the Foreign Office.

The association with Guinness was of lasting importance because by now Beaven had embarked on breeding new races of barley. He selected "pure lines" bred from a single ear, which led to the realization that it was not practicable to compare adjacent rows of different selections owing to the possibility of mutual interference. To overcome this and to equalise soil variation as much as possible the "chequerboard" system was devised and introduced in 1910. In this, Beaven was helped by W S Gosset, a Dublin based Guinness brewer and statistician of exceptional merit. Gosset was particularly focused on developing satisfactory designs for barley experiments and in the statistical analysis of their results. But even with this fairly robust selection technique, Beaven insisted on continuous field trials of the various selections as he sought to eliminate any sources of error in the results obtained.

From this intensive study, a number of true barley varieties were to emerge, but by far Beaven's greatest achievement was when he commenced hydridization and he crossed the barley variety 'Plumage' (of Swedish origin) with 'English Archer' to produce the hybrid 'Plumage Archer', which he first identified for selection as early as 1905. Following an extended and rigorous programme of field trials and further selection, this variety was eventually released to farmers for commercial production in 1914, and for the next forty years became the mainstay of malting barley production throughout the British Isles. Not only was 'Plumage Archer' the first genetically true variety of barley introduced to British farmers, but with it came a more consistent harvest quality, and an eye popping increase in crop yield of near 20%. Very quickly the name of Edwin Sloper Beaven was firmly established in the world of farming and brewing, acknowledged in 1922 by the award of an honorary doctorate (Hon. LL.D.) by the University of Cambridge.

'Plumage Archer' was not Beaven's only new variety of barley, in fact its commercial release was preceded in 1907 with 'Beaven's English Archer' and in 1909 with 'Beaven's Plumage', both more refined seed stocks of each of the parent stock. When 'Plumage Archer' was finally released for commercial production, Beaven had the foresight to call it 'Plumage Archer 1914', because he went on to improve the seed stock twice more, in 1924 and again in 1935, dating it accordingly. Finally in 1932 he introduced another hybrid 'Golden Archer', a cross of 'Plumage Archer' and the Irish derived 'Spratt Archer', which he further improved in 1938.

Beaven was a busy man, not just in his famous barley cage at the Boreham Road Barley Field but travelling anywhere and everywhere in pursuit of his knowledge of the genus. His annual barley tours which began in 1904 were quite an adventure, particularly for those he invited to travel with him. His famous Leon Bollee car with its high seats and open body was perfect for "farming over the hedge" as they drove along, and Beaven would propound his theories with his accustomed zeal, often paying more attention to the crops they passed than to the road ahead. These tours not only traversed the barley growing regions of England and Scotland, but also extended to lengthy drives across Germany (1906) and visits to the west coast of Ireland. Combined with the inevitable unscheduled delays for breakdowns with the

car (broken half shaft 3 miles from Durham in 1910) there is no doubt Margaret Beaven must have breathed a sigh of relief when her husband and his fellow passengers returned to Warminster safe and sound.

Beaven standing in front of his first car, a Jackson Dogcart, his three daughters on board.

Above: Beaven's famous barley cage at Boreham Road.
Right: Harvesting plots with a horse drawn binder at
Boreham Road.

In 1914, accompanied by his daughter Isobel and Professor T B Wood from Cambridge, Beaven joined the British Association world tour. Sailing with the Union Line, he toured Australia where he read a paper at a conference in Sydney before meeting barley growers in New Zealand and North America, when the tour was terminated abruptly upon the outbreak of World War I.

Back home, Beaven directed his energy towards the war effort, working for both the Ministries of Agriculture and Food, and for the Royal Society, specialising on the supply of brewing materials and focusing on nutritional problems. In respect of the latter he became a staunch and outspoken advocate of the wholemeal loaf. But once the war was ended Beaven returned to his barley breeding, determined to further improve yield and malting quality.

In order to stimulate the interest of farmers and brewers alike in his work he held 'At Homes' at the Boreham Road Barley Field in 1924, 1930 and 1936. These events, including lunch in an enormous marquee, were attended by many of the leading scientists from the fields of agriculture and brewing. Among them were the pre-eminent scientists and Fellows of the Royal Society, Professor H E Armstrong, and Sir Thomas Middleton who was the Deputy Director General of the Food Production Department (forerunner to DEFRA). It was Sir Thomas Middleton who pursuaded Beaven to write his book '*Barley - Fifty Years of Observation and Experiment*'.

Ears of barley mounted on a card, and inscribed in Beaven's own hand, 1910.
The ears of barley are, left to right: 'Plumage', 'Plumage Archer' and 'Archer.'

Coke of Norfolk *Sir John Bennett Lawes* *Dr. E S Beaven*

"No names will stand out more prominently."

At the 1936 'At Home' when submitting the loyal toast and paying tribute to Beaven's outstanding achievements, Lord Bledisloe proposed that "when the scientific history of British Agriculture comes to be written I cannot imagine that any names will stand out more prominently than those of Sir John Bennet Lawes (the originator of the artificial fertiliser) with his invaluable co-partner Joseph Gilbert, and Dr. E S Beaven. If any other name is to be associated, it would, in my judgement, be that of 'Coke of Norfolk', the first Earl of Leicester". High praise indeed, which ranks Beaven amongst the greatest agricultural pioneers of all time.

As well as an authoritative individual, as a man Beaven was a striking figure. Tall and spare, he dressed simply on all occasions to his own design – trousers and coat of grey tweed, with an all-round collar that buttoned close to the neck and dispensed with waistcoat and tie. His personality was stimulating, his sense of humour acute and infectious, and his generosity blunted the sting of his criticism. He was in every respect a figurehead, ideally suited to the Chairman's role, at the National Institute of Agricultural Botany (NIAB) in 1929, The Farmers Club in 1932, and back at the NIAB for a second tenure at the outbreak of war in 1939.

In his work, Beaven was original in thought and honest in execution regardless of his boundless enthusiasm for his particular subject. His approach to a problem was direct, his outlook was independent, and he maintained his point of view fearlessly and with tenacity. But if he was uncertain of his conclusions he would ever be the first to admit the work inconclusive and incomplete. To those around him it seemed his love of barley was founded on the beauty of the growing corn – his work was done for the sheer pleasure he had in it, and, remarkably, for him no material gain. He went a long way towards achieving his objectives, and at least left the nation his debtor in those lean years leading up to the Second World War when British farming had been sacrificed on the altar of imported food.

Beaven was blessed with a happy family life, including three daughters, the eldest of which, Alice, was her father's constant help and companion in his work to the end. His second daughter, Isobel, had married Professor T B Wood from Cambridge, and their only son, Beaven's only grandson, Thomas Beaven Wood, had been widely expected to carry on Beaven's work. That was until he was killed in action in Normandy in 1944.

So it was at Beaven's death in 1941, at the age of 84, that his daughter, Alice, together with his trustees, took charge of the business and the barley breeding programme in order to eventually steer it into the safe custody of its long time sponsor, Guinness, and into the third era of Warminster Maltings remarkable history.

Dr. and Mrs. Beaven celebrate their Golden Wedding.

Chapter 4

MALTING FOR GUINNESS IN THE 1950'S

The introduction of the combine harvester onto British farms in the 1950's was the beginning of a revolution in the way corn crops, including barley, were to be harvested and marketed. Prior to this, forever, the crops had been cut and bundled into sheaves, carted off the field and stored in stacks outdoors, normally in a stackyard back at the farmstead. These stacks were built to include the whole crop off one field, under a pitched roof of thatched straw to protect it against the weather. Then over the next 6-9 months a thrashing contractor would arrive on the farm with all the necessary equipment to thrash the grain from the straw, drawing off the corn in large hessian sacks for storage in the barn, and re-stacking the straw in the stackyard.

Main: Turning the 'green' malt by hand in 1950. Inset: by mechanical turner today.

This practice over time had dictated the regular flow of grain off farms into the market place, and fed a constant stream of newly thrashed offerings onto the Corn Exchanges that from the mid 19th Century existed in most market towns around Great Britain.

Salisbury Corn Exchange, opened 1859. John Strapp's design for the 'Market House' made a fine building, with its glass roof, wrought iron balconies, and its own railway siding.

The management at E S Beaven (Maltings) Ltd were required to procure only the best quality barleys, and so this meant a long drawn out buying campaign attending the Corn Exchanges at Salisbury (Tuesday) and Bristol (Thursday) from August through to Christmas. A measured purchasing campaign was required to not only feed production of malt from October to May, but also to ensure that at no stage quality was compromised.

At the time of Beaven's death in 1941, the business comprised of two malthouses in Warminster, a unique (by now) one-man malthouse off Market Place, and Pound Street, and the Montpelier Maltings in Bristol, all administered from the offices in East Street, Warminster. It was Beaven's long time assistant, Harold Wickham, who then took responsibility for the day-to-day running of the business, including purchasing the barley, and remained as

Presentation by Miss Alice Beaven to Harold Wickham on his retirement, 1952.

manager, when in 1947 a new company, E S Beaven (Maltings) Ltd was formed as a subsidiary of Arthur Guinness Son & Co (Great Britain) Ltd. Beaven's daughter, Miss Alice Beaven, was appointed a director of the new company in 1948 and remained on the board until her death in 1970. The barley breeding programme was transferred to a new site at Codford, just east of Warminster, managed by Tom Davis and a healthy budget from Guinness. But when Harold Wickham retired in 1952, it was Norman Oakey who was to replace him as manager of the Maltings and barley buyer, heading the administration team based at the East Street offices, overseeing a staff of up to twenty, including ten men at the Pound Street Maltings.

Each malting season, one of Oakey's first priorities was procuring his barley requirements, which he did by attending the aforementioned Corn Exchanges at Salisbury and Bristol. Samples of potential barley supplies would be shown to Oakey by those corn merchants attending the Corn Exchanges, and would be offered in small printed packets declaring an identification lot number, the quantity and variety of barley and the 'station'. The 'station' was the railway station closest to the barley crop, and a hangover from the days prior to the motor lorry when much of the barley was transported from farm to maltings by rail. Its continued declaration however was important as it denoted the geographical location from where the barley was grown, often helpful in encouraging maltsters to buy on the reputation of previous barley crops from that region. (For many years Docking station in Norfolk commanded enormous influence with Burton-on-Trent brewers, and we are told it was nothing to do with its proximity to the Sandringham Estate!).

Appraisal of the barley by Oakey was entirely by eye, something which experienced buyers could do quite quickly. Overall corn size and shape, colour of the grain, skin quality and physical damage (by weather) were quickly assimilated as the sample was repeatedly tipped into the palm of the buyers hand. Oakey might have bitten a kernel or two to expose the starch – a snowy white appearance was good, but a grey steely appearance denoted higher protein levels than preferred for brewing. Later in the 50's merchants and maltsters had the use of specially designed barley cutters which would slice fifty corns in half at a stroke, for instant examination of the starch colour.

Barley cutters

Above: A typical Corn Exchange scene, 1950's.
Top right: Market case containing barley samples.

The Guinness barley specification was of the highest quality – plump, fine skinned, mellow coloured grains with a snowy-white starch (denotes low grain nitrogen). In some seasons Oakey might reject far more samples presented to him than he ever took a second look at!

All barley was traded in quantities measured as 'quarters', a 'quarter' being four hundredweights (4 x 112lbs), and individual parcels would typically range from 25-225 quarters (5 – 45 tons). By today's standards this all appears to be very piecemeal, but each parcel represented one field which back in the 1950's was generally much smaller than today. Not only that, all the barley was conveyed in sacks, normally four bushel sacks (224 lbs nett) and lorries carried between 4 – 8 tons (40-80 sacks) at a time. 150 quarters of barley, which will squeeze onto a single bulk grain lorry today, required four lorries to move it back in 1953! From this it is not difficult to understand why Oakey's barley purchasing programme continued over 4-5 months – he had to buy between 4000 – 5000 tons of barley to cover both the Warminster and Bristol maltings, a total of probably around 200 separate parcels.

Norman Oakey's first trips to Bristol and Salisbury markets towards the end of July 1953 would have begun as an evaluation exercise to gauge the quality of the local barley crop over as wide an area as possible. According to the Barley Purchase Ledger of that campaign, we

Norman Oakey's barley purchase ledger from 1953.

can judge from the first price paid, 75 quarters bought on July 30th from Goodenoughs of Reading Ltd. at 129/6d per quarter, either the quality was slightly better than the previous year, or Oakey was concerned about booking good barleys when he saw them should the overall quality not quite match up. In fact the records illustrate that Oakey maintained this price structure right through to the New Year when on January 12th, he purchased 78 quarters from Christopher Hill Ltd at 132/6d per quarter.

Back on Pound Street, a team of ten men were employed to run the malting process led by foreman W George (Bill) Baker. Two men were permanently employed at the barley reception and known as the 'barley men'. It was they who received the barley deliveries purchased by Oakey, and they were responsible first of all for drying this barley from around 16% down to 13% moisture, ready for the steeping process that followed. There were two reasons for drying the barley, one was to ensure it was all at the same moisture content prior to steeping, which in turn ensured homogenous water uptake, and the other was to break the natural 'dormancy' of the grains which might otherwise demonstrate a reluctance to germinate on the floors. Drying of the barley was carried out on the coal fired 'sweater' kiln, adjacent to the first floor barley store, where the 'barley men' spent their days barrowing, tipping, refilling and stacking four bushel sacks of barley, prior to tipping them again, as required, through hatches in the floor, into the steeping cisterns beneath. Once in the steep, the process of modifying the barley into malt began.

The steeping process would take approximately 3 days when the barley was immersed three times in water, for 12 hours at a time, followed by 12 hours of draining, allowing the grain to 'breathe'. Control of the water temperature is critical to this process, and Pound Street's own well provided, and still provides, water at a constant 52°F throughout the year, which is ideal for steeping. At the end of the steeping process the moisture content of the barley has been raised from 13% up to 45% and the weight of the barley which started as 10 tons of dry grain has now been increased to 16 tons which has to be shovelled out in preparation for spreading on the floors.

Today emptying the steeps still involves a lot of shovelling, and despite the addition of grain augers it is still one of the hardest jobs in the maltings. In 1953 there were no grain augers, and it was all shovelling, involving up to four or five men working alongside each other. First of all they shovelled the wet grain onto the 'couch' between the cistern and the floors, where it remained for a few hours, sufficient to generate heat and stimulate 'chitting' (germination).

The next stage involved shovelling the wet grain again, onto the upper and lower floors before spreading the grain out, making an even bed which would vary in depth from three to twelve inches, depending on prevailing air temperatures. The wet grain was transported across the floors using 'Boby' barrows, specially designed by brewing engineers Robert Boby & Son of Bury St Edmunds. The narrow, large circumference wheeled barrows were light and very manoeuvrable, and are still sometimes used by the maltsters at Warminster today.

While on the floor, the barley was intermittently 'worked' in order to maintain an even temperature and moisture content, to supply fresh oxygen and remove waste carbon dioxide, and to control the growth of the rootlets and prevent them matting together. In 1953 working the floor was done by turning the grain over with wooden shovels, or more lightly with wooden forks, and by drawing by hand a metal bladed malt plough through the bed of grain. When to carry out these procedures was the skill and judgement of the foreman and his deputy, and one man of their team would work only at night in order to attend these needs which were continuous, 24 hours per day, 7 days a week.

After five or six days on the floor, examination of the grain would reveal whether all the starch had finally broken down into sugars, or whether it needed a few more hours. Once this process was complete, growth had to be quickly stopped. This was done by transferring the 'green' malt, as it is known, to the kiln.

In 1953 each pair of floors had its own kiln. Floor 2 had a brand new oil fired 'Winkler' pressure kiln which had been installed the previous year, but Floors 1, 3 and 4 were still using the original conical coal fired structures, and these required a fireman to run them.

Fired by 'arsenic free' anthracite supplied from the collieries in South Wales, the coal fired kilns were slow and labour intensive. The whole drying and curing process would take around 72 hours, with the 'green' malt loaded to a depth of no more than 7 to 8 inches and turned by hand at least twice a day. This was done firstly with wooden tine forks, and as the malt dried, with wooden shovels. If emptying the steeps was regarded as hard work, turning the kilns was harder, having to endure the heat and humidity generated above the malt.

The new, now gas fired, 'Winkler' kiln and elevator;
original coal fired kiln (inset).

The art of 'firing' the coal kilns very much depended on the skill and experience of 'firemen' like Paddy O'Reilly to produce the right amount of heat at each stage of the two stage process. For the first 36 hours (the first stage), the objective was to halt germination, and stabilize the enzyme structure of the malt. This was also the stage which influenced the colour of the end product, temperatures of 90 – 100°F producing pale malt, and 120°F required for the darker malt demanded by Guinness. Importantly, this first drying stage reduced the moisture content of the malt from 40% right down to just 4%.

For the second stage, Paddy O'Reilly would raise the heat to between 180 – 220°F in order to cure the malt and enhance its flavour. He would achieve this by excluding the draughts employed in the first stage as much as possible. The installation of the oil fired fan assisted 'Winkler' kiln heralded the beginning of the end of the traditional coal fired method, because malt could now be loaded to a depth of 30 inches, dried and cured in 22 hours with no manual 'turning' or attention necessary. This kiln remains in use to this day and now services the total malt production at Pound Street.

The final process after the malt had been shovelled off the kiln was the screening process, when the dried rootlets, known as 'malt culms' were removed from the corn. In 1953 the 'malt screen', housed on the ground floor of the malt store facing Pound Street, was the oldest piece of equipment used in the maltings. This was another product of Robert Boby & Son of Bury St Edmunds and was supplied new to Baileys Maltings in Warminster on 13th January 1887. Purchased by E S Beaven three years later and installed in Pound Street, it consisted of a rotating barrel of four wire drum sections with metal paddles inside. Manned by Jack Wheeler the finished malt was drawn off the malt screen into four bushel hessian sacks, ready for loading onto lorries for the short journey to Warminster station. From here the malt travelled by rail to the Guinness Park Royal brewery in London. The 'malt culms' were also put into sacks and weighed for distribution to local farmers for cattle feed.

The malting process was continuous through the autumn of 1953, not even stopping for Christmas and through to May 1954 when the beginning of summer temperatures would have eventually dictated the need to call a halt. As the month of May progressed and the prevailing air temperature increased Bill Baker and his team would be spreading the wet barley on the floors at even shallower depths and all the window shutters would be wide open to ensure the temperature in the grain was contained at no more than 70°F. Come 'blazing' June, this would never work.

Instead thoughts turned to repairs and to maintenance, and of course holidays. Of the former there were some elevators and conveyors to be serviced, an overhaul of the malt screen, and kilns to be swept. In particular, the perforated floor tiles of the coal fired kilns would need unblocking and cleaning to ensure optimum performance when malting restarted. There was also a lot of painting, particularly inside, and the 'barley men' had hundreds of sacks to repair, using home cut patches to cover the holes chewed through the hessian by mice.

*Paddy O'Reilly firing Kiln No. 2, 1950. This was the kiln that
gave way to the new oil fired 'Winkler' pressure kiln.*

THE MALTING PROCESS
BEAVEN'S MALTINGS, POUND STREET, WARMINSTER

Based on original photographs, 1950.

10 **LOADING THE KILN INTO THE MALT STORE**
This was a very uncomfortable job only partially helped by the large extractor fans (kilns 3 & 4) which had succeeded the conical roofs (kilns 1 & 2).

11 **FRESH MALT STORED IN THE MALT STORE**
The upper floor of the store was sub-divided into storage bays, with two storage bays per kiln for two different grades/batches of malt.

12 **DRAWING THE FINISHED MALT INTO SACKS OFF THE MALT SCREEN**
The malt screen separated the dried shoots, known as malt culms from the malt grains, which were then weighed into

7 **TRANSFERRING 'GREEN' MALT FROM THE LOWER TO THE UPPER FLOOR FOR LOADING ONTO THE KILN**
In 1950 there was no elevator, just continuous shovelling.

8 **LOADING THE KILN**
Both floors had to be loaded onto the kiln bed, and levelled, as quickly as possible.

9 **FIREMAN STOKING THE KILN**
Drying the 'green' malt took up to 72 hours in a two stage process when management of the heat was key to the colour and flavour of the malt

4 **TRANSPORTING THE WET BARLEY ACROSS THE FLOORS USING A 'BOBY' BARROW**

The large circumference, narrow wheeled malt barrow was highly manoeuvrable.

5 **PLOUGHING THE 'GREEN' MALT**

The maltster's hand drawn 'plough' separates and aerates the 'green' malt in the advanced stages of modification.

6 **TURNING THE 'GREEN' MALT**

Using a six pronged wooden fork the 'green' malt is turned in order to manage the temperature in the early

1 **HOISTING THE SACKS OF BARLEY INTO THE BARLEY STORE**

Typically delivered via loads of 7 tons (70 x 4 bushel sacks) accurately weighed by the farmer when the sacks were filled.

2 **BARLEY DRYING ON THE 'SWEATER' KILN**

Variable moisture content of barley delivered from the farms had to be addressed for safe long term storage.

3 **SPLITTING THE WET BARLEY ONTO THE UPPER AND LOWER FLOORS.**

Looking back, Guinness' attention to the outer fabric of the maltings, which it never owned, was less than perfect, and could never have envisaged malting continuing for as long as it did. In fact we know that by the 1970's they had gone a long way towards finalizing plans for a brand new malting plant, east of Warminster, at Codford. Had this come to fruition, they probably expected the Pound Street site to be demolished, like so many other traditional 'floor' maltings at the time, and so any external repairs were more of a 'patching' exercise than any determined attempt to preserve the buildings.

That the new plant at Codford was never built is perhaps less surprising than that Pound Street continued malting, but continue malting it did, and very successfully, under a management team led by Lawrence Hampton, managing director, of E S Beaven (Maltings) Ltd and Oakey's successor, Hugh Turner, executive director based at the East Street offices, Warminster. Both these men warrant recognition.

Lawrence Hampton joined Guinness in the early 60's taking responsibility for the combined malting operation, as well as being responsible for all raw materials procurement for the brewing company. This was a challenging role, but despite this, Hampton ensured that he maintained a regular presence at each end of the malting business, in Wiltshire at Warminster as well as in Norfolk at Diss and Great Yarmouth.

Lawrence Hampton inspecting barley prior to harvest.

Following harvest Hampton took on a particularly busy schedule of attendances at all the relevant Corn Exchanges. Beginning with London's Mark Lane market on Monday, he would then join Hugh Turner at Salisbury Corn Exchange on Tuesday, and then catching up with John Moody from Diss at Bury St Edmunds market on Wednesday, Bristol on Thursday, and the busy Diss Exchange on Friday afternoon. He would keep this up week after week because his overall monitoring of the barley crop countrywide provided an important steer to the regional purchasing policies adopted by Turner and Moody. Hampton's other outstanding contribution was that he skilfully protected the malting business from any overbearing influence that might otherwise have been imposed upon it by its formidable parent company, almost certainly another contributory factor to the longevity of Pound Street's malthouses.

Artefacts from the Corn Exchange – market desk, market case,
and maltsters' aid, the hand-held barley cutter.

Hugh Turner was a local boy who joined Beaven's at the beginning of 1950 as a laboratory assistant, earning £1.15.0 per week. His early responsibilities involved collecting malt samples from Pound Street on his bicycle, and on 'mashing days' he would also collect ice from the local fishmonger, as the malt extract determination in those days involved cooling with ice. Turner quickly became an expert at predicting the malt quality based on the amount of force he had to apply to the laboratory hand mill grinding the malt. He forever regarded it as a backward step when the Institute of Brewing instigated the fitting of electric motors to all laboratory mills.

"Turner was the last direct link with the Beaven family."

During his long career with 'ESB Ltd' Turner mastered every office and production job at Warminster, and was made Maltings manager in 1971, and a director of the company in 1977. He was also the last direct link with the Beaven family, and in his early days used to take tea with Miss Alice Beaven whilst she signed the company cheques.

After 44 years with the company it was Turner who had the difficult task of announcing the closure of the Maltings to the staff and local community. But when Guinness made this decision which also signalled the retirement of both Hampton and Turner, it is unlikely that any of them reckoned on the response from some of their employees. Led by Chris Garratt, Turner's assistant manager, the maltsters at Pound Street were defiant and far from ready to put down their tools.

Harvesting large scale barley trials at Warminster – 1950's.

Chapter 5

LIFE AFTER GUINNESS

"Guinness Pull the Plug: Maltings to Close"

ran the headlines in the Warminster Journal of 20th May 1994. "It's a very sad day" said Bill Spears, Guinness' director of public affairs in London. "We had very much hoped that we could find someone to take on the business as a going concern. Although we have looked very carefully, no-one could be found." Spears was wrong. That person could be found,

Front page Warminster Journal – Friday 20th May 1994.

and what is more, that person sat right under Guinness' very nose. Chris Garratt had joined the company in 1975, straight from school, and had trained as a maltster, and that's what he wanted to go on doing.

The morning after Garratt had been given the bad news over dinner at the Red Lion in Heytesbury from Lawrence Hampton, managing director of E S Beaven (Maltings) Ltd, Hampton chose to call on David Miles at the former Guinness Barley Research Station at Codford. Miles was currently leasing the Codford site from Guinness, from where he operated his own agricultural research based company, Westcrop Ltd. Prior to this relatively new enterprise, Miles had been employed by Guinness based at Codford, and had in effect been part of the Warminster team. Shocked by the news, that night Miles phoned Garratt and a plan of campaign was begun.

In his favour, Garratt had been offered employment by Guinness through to October, with responsibility for the day to day administration of the closure of the Pound Street Maltings and all that it entailed. What it did entail was frequent visits to the Park Royal Brewery and access to Guinness personnel, including David Holmes, head of raw materials. Garratt outlined his plans to Holmes, namely, with the financial backing of Miles' Westcrop Ltd, to carry on at Pound Street, producing malt for local breweries, effectively re-starting the original business of 'sales maltster' abandoned by Beaven 80 years before. Holmes generous response was "We cannot see you fail" and there and then awarded Garratt a 300 tonnes per annum malt contract to supply Park Royal. Suddenly, the new order book had been opened, and what is more, production of Guinness malt would continue at Pound Street after all!

This was the sort of start that Garratt needed, so when Hampton, now retired, gave Garratt a clutch of introductions to local breweries, Garratt was quickly in touch with all the respective head brewers, and the order book began to grow. Following sorties to the breweries, often accompanied by Hampton, Garratt soon agreed malt supply contracts with nearby Eldridge Pope of Dorchester, Gibbs Mew of Salisbury, Hall & Woodhouse of Blandford Forum, the new Hop Back Brewery of Downton, and Ushers of Trowbridge.

At this point, Garratt's prime concern was to get into production as quickly as possible following harvest of the 1994 barley crop. But before he could do that Westcrop Ltd needed to takeover at 39 Pound Street. Agreement was reached with Guinness to purchase all the fixtures and fittings, and a two-year lease of the site was drawn up with the Trustees of E S Beaven.

Next, four of the six maltsters were re-employed, including Jerry Curtis the current foreman, and Alison Hillier, who had worked alongside Garratt in the East Street offices, came along to cover administration, and to help Garratt with barley and malt analysis in the

Westcrop laboratory. Then Steve Musselwhite, a local haulage contractor, who for a long time had been engaged to deliver barley to the Maltings, was persuaded to swap his bulk grain lorry for a curtain sided flat bed lorry, to deliver the malt in bags to the new brewery customers.

All that done, the next major challenge was to convert the malting process back to delivering the finished product in bags. For the last 50 years most of the production had been devoted

20 years of bulk barley in, bulk malt out.

to a single specification pale malt for Guinness, and for the last 20 years delivery of that malt had been in bulk, in a customised bulk malt lorry. The logistics had been simple – a 1000 tonne flat store at the back of the maltings was kept full of a single grade of a single variety of barley, and bulk malt storage at the front of the maltings was sufficient to fill just three to four lorries each week.

From now on, Garratt was already dealing with two different varieties of barley and six different specifications of malt, and this spectrum was set to widen. All this had to be stored individually, and the finished products, other than the Guinness malt, had to be weighed into 50 kg sacks, stitched and stacked on pallets, awaiting delivery. This all required new engineering, although much of the hardware was 'acquired' or purchased secondhand. Improvisation was everywhere, even the traditional Avery scales which had been tucked away in a corner for the last 25 years, were dragged out for a renewed, if brief, lease of life! Then last, but not quite least, Garratt required an office. The former East Street offices had been vacated and returned to the Beaven Trustees, and so more improvisation was required, on the ground floor of the second former malt store, fronting Pound Street. Although the roof above was leaking, this was the only space available, and so partition walls and a lick of paint created two cubicles from which the new venture could now be managed.

So in September 1994, despite all the proclamation by Guinness to the contrary, malting again re-started at the Pound Street Maltings, and 150 years of production continued to clatter on. The people of Warminster were delighted, and at all times supportive. They took pride in 'their' maltings and were particularly buoyed up, as the Brits always are, when the underdog (Garratt) prevailed against the mighty conglomerate (Guinness). Neighbours, in the surrounding cottages, all made this known to Garratt, as each went about their daily business, and this all served to galvanise the determination of the new management team.

"150 years of production continued to clatter on."

But if Garratt's new customer list was impressive, and it was, the challenge that lay ahead of him was even more formidable than he imagined. For within the next 10 years, four of his first six customers, including Guinness' Park Royal Brewery, would announce their closure. Unlike Warminster's Maltings, these great establishments would actually shut and disappear for ever!

"The traditional Avery scales".

The long standing history a...
experience of growing...
crop, field trials and han...
evaluation of samples...
only the very best bar...
in the maltings eac...

The Maltings...
malt using...
has kept...

Traditional
Floor Malting

WARMINSTER
MALTINGS

Lager Malt

Pale Ale Malt

Mild Ale Malt

Crystal Malts

Roasted Malts

WARMINSTER MALTINGS

Chris Garratt's first Sales Brochure.

Chapter 6
OLD LINKS, NEW LINKS

"…Garratt soldiered on …" Chris Garratt 1994.

Following an encouraging start in the autumn of 1994, Chris Garratt's new business had to work hard to make up the sales tonnages necessary to achieve a viable enterprise. It took more than a handful of smaller brewers to equate to the sales volume of an Eldridge Pope order, or a Gibbs Mew order, but Garratt soldiered on, and bit by bit the business grew.

So did Garratt's confidence, to the point that when a new lease for the Pound Street site had to be negotiated he persuaded the Beaven Trustees to sell, and David Miles to buy. The buildings were in a poor state of repair and represented an unacceptable liability to the Trustees had the new tenants begun making demands. Not only that, these Grade 2 listed buildings were now recognised as of significant importance, and failure of the malting business might have precipitated an Enforcement Order for repairs of a substantial nature. But if after 150 years the link between the Beaven family and Miss Alice's "grandfather's old malthouses" had finally been broken, at least the maltings were "still in use" and while that continued, the spirit of E S Beaven would always be there.

Then the next link to be broken was that with Guinness. In 1997, after just three years under Garratt's new management, the Guinness contract came to an end when all the group's malt production was finally transferred to Scotland. This association with the global brewer had continued for nearly 100 years, but brewing technology was changing, and Warminster's technology was not.

"Maris Otter — a much revered malting barley."

However, the breach was quickly filled by brewers Marston's of Burton on Trent who placed a contract for 'Maris Otter' malt for their leading brand, Pedigree bitter. All the 'Maris Otter' barley grown in the south of England was grown by farmers contracted to the Hampshire based grain merchant, Robin Appel Ltd. Back in 1990 Robin Appel had been persuaded to lead an initiative to preserve the production of 'Maris Otter' barley, a variety first introduced onto Britain's farms in 1966. Although a much revered malting barley within the brewing industry, it was well past its 'sell by' date with farmers, who could now grow much higher yielding varieties. By 1995 Appel, together with a Norfolk barley merchant, had exclusive rights to the production and marketing of 'Otter' barley. So Appel was called upon to supply the 'Maris Otter' barley to Warminster for the Marston contract, and quietly a new link was formed.

By 1999, it became clear to Appel that Westcrop Ltd's financial backing for the Warminster Maltings business was proving inadequate, and at Garratt's suggestion a meeting between, Miles and Appel was arranged. Appel did not pull his punches; he told Miles that if he was prepared to consider an offer for the malting business, then one would be forthcoming. But Miles was cautious, and Garratt had to struggle on. Two years later, however when

Appel's credit against barley supplies exceeded acceptable limits, Appel repeated his offer somewhat more forcefully.

On 13th February 2001, contracts were finally exchanged between Miles and Appel and the new business of Warminster Maltings Ltd changed hands 'lock, stock and barrel.' So began another transformation of the business. Appel was sure that the logical development of his 'Maris Otter' barley initiative was the harnessing of traditional malting capacity, and the two together, he felt, could turn the Maltings in Pound Street into one of Britain's lead-ing malt suppliers to the emerging small brewery sector. He had also identified what he considered as a hidden shrine within the nation's brewing heritage.

"Cometh the hour, cometh the man".

Chapter 7

A New Era Begins

Robin Appel joins the staff of Warminster Maltings Ltd – February 2001.

The sun streamed through the windows of Number 1, London Road, Southampton that afternoon of February 13th 2001, as Robin Appel sat in silence opposite Andrew Heathcock, corporate business partner at solicitors, Paris Smith and Randall. They were awaiting a phone call from Warminster solicitors, Middleton and Upsall, to signal the transfer of the Maltings from David Miles to Appel. At 2.35 pm the phone call came – contracts had been exchanged. Appel was born on the 13th (July) and always regarded the number as lucky for him. Events today, of all days, had to be a good omen he felt.

The following morning Appel presented himself triumphantly at 39, Pound Street, declaring the beginning of a new era for the Maltings. Garratt was equally excited, but the formal introduction of Appel to the working maltsters was only met with looks that grunted "We will believe that when we see it!" Appel was insistent "I will not let you down!"

There was much to be done completing the arrangements for the transfer of the business – new bank accounts, insurance, debts to be settled, new accounts opened and, of course, a formal press announcement. But, before talking to the press Appel was determined to announce his acquisition to the malting industry in person. This meant a drive around Britain to quietly tell them himself. After all, all these businesses were customers of Robin Appel Ltd for malting barley supplies, and Appel was concerned that no 'conflict of interest' should be perceived.

As it turned out, quite the opposite was true. Beginning in Simon Simpson's office at Simpsons Malt Ltd, Berwick-upon-Tweed, on the morning of February 20th, Appel was welcomed warmly and wished the best of luck. That same afternoon, Ian Hall, purchasing director, of Thomas Fawcett & Sons Ltd of Castleford, Yorkshire pointed out to Appel that it was "a nice business to be in." Two days later, Bob King at Crisp Malting Group, Gt. Ryburgh, Norfolk indicated that there was a question mark overhanging the future of their own 'floor' maltings which had been brought out of redundancy less than 10 years before. He inferred that far from any "conflict" there might even be some common interest here. Alan Ridealgh at Muntons plc, at Stowmarket, in Suffolk saw Appel's acquisition as "a reason for working ever closer together!" At the end of that week when he returned home, Appel was quietly well pleased with the reaction of the UK's malting businesses – he felt he had just joined a club where he was not only going to be very happy, but also amongst good friends!

The initial euphoria over, back at Warminster, the size of Appel's task in order to turn the business around began slowly to sink in. On each of his weekly visits as he explored the complex, the enormous extent of the dilapidations became more and more apparent.

It was the consequence of previous circumstances. Firstly, the previous offices, situated at the other end of town in East Street, where the management ran the maltings at arms length and probably largely ignorant of the poor state of repair of the fabric of Pound Street. Then of course, secondly, back in the 70's the grand plan to build the new maltings at Codford. Had that happened, it might have resulted in the total destruction of the Pound Street site, making way for housing! Of course, there were those that wondered whether Appel had a 'Plan B'

(housing) up his sleeve and an early visitor to the Maltings in 2001 was Amber Patrick, consultant to English Heritage. Miss Patrick had a particular interest in 'floor' maltings and had chronicled many of the remaining structures throughout England in the 70's and 80's before they 'disappeared' finally and she had visited Warminster on more than one occasion. On this latest visit she listened to Appel and Garratt's enthusiastic plans, but made it quite clear to Appel before she left that in the event of any plans "beyond malting" the Grade 2 listed structure could become Grade 2* in just 48 hours! Appel knew what that implied and was bemused by this gentle threat – there was no Plan B!

The only plan was one to put Warminster Maltings Ltd firmly on the map as the preferred malt supplier to the small, independent brewery sector, the so-called micro-breweries. To this end, already, halfway through Appel's second and successful attempt to buy Warminster, The Beeston Malting Company Ltd, at Beeston, Nottingham, a 'floor' maltings and tiny subsidiary of Scottish Courage, had announced its closure at the end of December 2000. This was a gift to Appel's plans and Garratt quickly set about winning Beeston's customers over to Warminster malt.

At the same time to the south, a good friend, Richard Wheeler, who ran Tuckers 'floor' maltings at Newton Abbott, Devon, had been quite open about his 'waiting list' of potential customers. This too warranted investigation, and mail shots were targeted accordingly, with Garratt systematically following up on the phone, or dropping by "when passing". Slowly but surely new orders began to build.

In the autumn of 2001 the first programme of capital expenditure began with the creation of a new bulk handling system for both barley coming into the maltings, and, a battery of bulk bins for finished malt products on their way out. The new barley intake facility was particularly critical as prior to this grain lorries had been taking up to 4 hours to discharge their load, a timescale quite unacceptable in 2001, and one which not only attracted bills from hauliers for "excess waiting time", but was actually persuading some hauliers to refuse to accept instructions for the Maltings. Installation of the new bulk handling system was going to disrupt production from time to time, and a strategy for overcoming this had to be devised. At the meeting Appel had with Crisp Maltings Group earlier that year in February, the subject of their 'floor' maltings at Gt. Ryburgh, Norfolk had been brought up. It was contracted to Marstons, the Burton-on-Trent brewer, for the production of malt for their all successful Pedigree bitter beer. But, Marstons had just been bought by the expanding

First capital project – new barley and malt bins.

Today's core business – bespoke 1 tonne pallets of crushed malt, shrink-wrapped for despatch.

Wolverhampton & Dudley Breweries plc and it had been decided that the expense of a dedicated sub-contracted maltings, and what's more a dedicated 'floor' maltings, was one that Pedigree bitter would have to do without. So the contract with Crisp was terminated.

Now the staff running the Crisp 'floor' maltings were fully trained floor maltsters having begun their careers in Diss, Norfolk working for Guinness at E S Beaven's former East Anglian maltings. They and Garratt had all been to the same school, so to speak, and showed a common passion for malting. If malt production, for Warminster Maltings, needed to be temporarily sub-contracted, Crisp was the perfect partner and the opportunity was staring Appel and Garratt in the face.

Then in the spring of 2002, Appel's business plan received yet another welcome boost. The Campaign for Real Ale (CAMRA) had been lobbying for 20 years for relief on the beer tax paid by small brewers, to enable a more level playing field within the beer market where the economies of scale enjoyed by the larger breweries delivered an enormous competitive advantage. On April 18th, Gordon Brown, Chancellor of the Exchequer, announced the introduction of Small Brewers Relief (SBR) for breweries producing less than 30,000 hectolitres of beer per annum, to commence in

Victory for small brewers after 20-year crusade
MICRO JOY AS GORDON CUTS DUTY

by **TED BRUNING**

BUDGET day was a day of celebration for Britain's 350 microbreweries as Chancellor Gordon Brown finally handed them the duty cut they have been fighting to get for nearly 20 years.

From this summer – "in time for the World Cup," said Mr Brown – brewers who produce less than 3,000 barrels a year will get their duty cut by half – a saving of about £40 a barrel. Brewers producing up to 18,000 barrels will get a graded discount on duty that could save them £120,000 a year.

Society of Independent Brewers spokesman Nick Stafford of Yorkshire's Hambleton Ales said: "This is excellent news. It's great – you can't say otherwise.

"We actually argued for the limit to be set higher, but the Treasury wasn't having any of it. Still, we are finally going to reap the rewards of years and years of campaigning, and it will make a significant difference to the chances of growth for hundreds of small breweries."

Mr Stafford predicted that many micros would use the duty saving to buy pubs of their own.

But he warned: "Those that do will find that running pubs is very different from brewing and is very hard work indeed. SIBA will be on hand with commercial and professional advice on buying and running pubs and there is a lot of hard work ahead for us."

He also predicted that many publicans would start up their own breweries. "They'll find there are many pitfalls, though," he said. "To sell their beer they'll have to brew better than their competitors.

"Still, the best of luck to anyone who fancies setting up their own breweries – we look forward to the competition."

One brewery that has already decided how to invest its saving is Fisherrow of Edinburgh, which plans to buy an additional dray and employ telesales staff.

Head brewer Iain Turnbull said: "This long overdue concession will provide a level playing field to allow this section of the industry to compete with the large conglomerates and should ultimately provide increased employment opportunities and growth."

CAMRA hailed the duty cut as a move towards healthier competition and greater consumer choice. Head of Campaigns Mike Benner said the change would remove a major barrier to market entry for micros and added: "Hopefully we will see a far more interesting range of locally-brewed beers on pub bars from now on."

As well as the cut for micros, Mr Brown froze duty on beer, wine, and spirits for the second year running. He also cut duty on cider by a halfpenny a pint and raised it by 11p a bottle on spirit-based alcopops.

'CAMRA's official newspaper 'Whats Brewing' front page – May 2002, the announcement of SBR.

June of that year. Appel and Garratt were beer judging at The Maltings Beer Festival at Newton Abbott, Devon on the day this news broke, where they were surrounded by one of the largest gatherings of brewers and beer aficionados to get together each year in the south-west of England. The atmosphere immediately turned from bonhomie to carnival. Gordon Brown had delivered a radical shake-up for Britain's brewing industry, and one which many predicted could become the role model for the whole of the food industry in due course.

"The atmosphere immediately turned to carnival."

Appel and Garratt calculated what the financial implications of SBR to a typical Warminster customer might be, and were surprised at the eye popping figures they came up with. What would brewers do with all this cash? They were meant to use it to discount their beer in the market place in order to compete for sales, but since many of them were producing such good beer that was not as necessary as perhaps Gordon Brown had been led to believe. In that case the likelihood was that some of this money would be directed at re-investment in the brewery. Re-investment in this case invariably means more capacity which, of course, would mean more malt!

Chris Garratt celebrating at The Maltings Beer Festival.

The race was on; could Warminster Maltings pull itself together in time for this emerging excitement? If it could, would it even be able to meet the demand? This business needed far more than just a new bulk handling facility – it needed a whole new administration block, not only suitable for receiving customers and other interested parties, but also, and most particularly, designed for the modern and professional management of a high profile business.

Chapter 8
THE FIRST RESTORATION PROJECT

When Garratt was obliged to leave his original East Street headquarters in 1994, he and his assistant Alison Hillier had decamped to Pound Street and created two small offices on the ground floor of a redundant malt store, entranced from Pound Street itself. The facilities were far from ideal, lacking space, natural light or much protection from the elements – the roof above them was in a very bad way, and when it rained, water literally poured in. The two cubicles, for they were little more than that, were barely big enough for each occupant and the accompanying facilities were of an equally poor standard. Something had to be done.

Restoration of the redundant malt store and kiln No. 1.

In 2002 Appel began to cast around for help, seeking not only advice from surveyors and architects but at the same time looking for available grant money that would make the financial management of any project more viable. Jarrod Hill, a young architect specialising in the restoration of old buildings emerged as the professional partner Appel sought, and grant money from the Departments of Environment, Food and Rural Affairs (DEFRA) and from The Warminster Civic Trust provided the financial impetus for a project to proceed. This project was to completely restore the redundant malt store, in which Garratt's offices were housed, and to create a brand new open plan office on the first floor, leading into a spacious new laboratory, with reception rooms and complete facilities for all the staff on the ground floor. In order to do this the building had to be evacuated, gutted, the roof stripped and the floor plan reconfigured.

It was a major project and perhaps partly in anticipation of all this upheaval Alison Hillier tendered her resignation to Garratt after 30 years service with the Maltings. However, Garratt replaced Alison with two new recruits, and so Stephen Pyne (Office) and Malcolm Smith (Laboratory) both began their new working careers at Pound Street housed in portakabins adjacent to what closely resembled a bombsite.

The refurbishment project began in June of 2003, in fine weather, and proceeded apace. But as with all old buildings, particularly ones immediately adjacent to others, the unforeseen was

a regular occurrence. None, however, was more dramatic than when the roof of Kiln No.1 immediately adjacent to the malt store, completely caved in. Fortunately, Appel was on holiday in Italy at the time, but the restoration of this roof became another major expense on the long list of 'extras' that came about as the project progressed.

"The occasion was a triumph and a landmark event."

Nevertheless, the refurbishment was completed by December, just in time to hold a pre-Christmas reception for all involved, neighbours, local dignitaries and friends of the maltings. So, on the evening of December 11th, with the paint barely dry, guests foregathered in the refurbished malt store, where they

Mrs. Oldham cuts the ribbon with Robin Appel looking on.

Refurbishment complete – lower Pound Street, 2004.

sipped champagne, were taken on guided tours of the malt floors, all being worked that evening, and were also treated to musical recitals by the very talented young musicians from Warminster School. But, most particularly, the new facility was formally opened by Mrs. Susan Oldham, one of E S Beaven's granddaughters.

The occasion was a triumph and a landmark event for the Maltings. It made a statement that the business was serious and confident. When Appel addressed the gathering that evening he declared that the customer base was already close to 200 brewers. In just 3 years the Warminster Maltings brand was being stamped all over the brewing industry, not just across the UK but right across the world.

A brand new open plan office on the first floor.

Chapter 9

'PLUMAGE ARCHER' COMES HOME

David Wilson and Robin Appel in a field of 'Plumage Archer', Duchy Home Farm.

That special expedition around Britain's maltsters in February 2001 made by Appel immediately he had bought the Maltings appeared to yield a second dividend in the summer of 2003. Simpsons Malt Ltd of Berwick-upon-Tweed was just one of only four UK maltsters, including Warminster Maltings, with Organic accreditation to produce Organic malt. Simpsons' designated Organic maltings at Pontefract was due to close, and they decided rather than re-locate the Organic production to another site, they would negotiate a transfer of the sales portfolio to one of their fellow Maltsters. They chose Warminster Maltings.

What the portfolio lacked in quantity, it made up for in quality. There were two not insubstantial supply contracts to two major brewers and there was also a contract to make malt from the barley grown by Sir Paul McCartney on his farm in East Sussex. There was another similar contract for the barley grown by HRH The Prince of Wales at his Duchy Home Farm next to Highgrove, at Tetbury in Gloucestershire. The Prince's chosen variety was 'Plumage Archer'!

The Duchy Home Farm initiative had come about a few years before from a dialogue between the farm's manager, David Wilson and the head brewer at the Wychwood Brewery in Oxfordshire. It had been David's idea to gather samples of different barley varieties, both from current and archive seed stocks, and then to taste the raw barley and select the most preferred flavour for commercial production at Duchy Home Farm. It should be said that David Wilson expected to be persuaded by one of the traditional varieties of barley in line with the whole ethos of the farming policy preferred by the Prince. Having discovered 'Plumage Archer' to be the outstanding choice, seed was acquired from the national seed bank, and the barley was then grown exclusively for a new beer brewed by the Wychwood Brewery in Oxfordshire.

However, by 2003, the Duchy Originals food label was having a major impact within the premium food sector. The original concept had been to produce a range of traditional, luxury quality foods that could be originated from right across the Duchy Estate as well as the Prince's own Home Farm. Beginning with an oat biscuit from David Wilson's farmed oats at Tetbury, labelled products from the annual wheat and barley harvest were also on the agenda. So Duchy Originals agreed with Wychwood Brewery to substitute Wychwood's own label with a new Duchy Ale brewed from the 'Plumage Archer' grown at Duchy Home Farm and now to be malted at Warminster Maltings.

Appel took much interest in the crop of 'Plumage Archer' that summer, and there was much good humoured debate as to whether the variety was still true to type or whether it had reverted back to its parentage of 'Plumage' and 'Archer'. Fortunately, back at Warminster, Mrs. Oldham had discovered some forgotten treasures, handed down from her grandfather, E S Beaven, and amongst them was a postcard to which ears of the barley from the parent stock and the progeny had been glued, all clearly labelled in Beaven's own hand (see page 23). The 'Plumage Archer' in the field was predominantly true to type!

"99 years after its introduction."

A glass of 'Plumage Archer'!

Following a successful harvest at Tetbury that August, the project was launched the following autumn. Prior to this, David Wilson had not made the connection between 'Plumage Archer' and Warminster Maltings, and although Garratt, was aware of the Wychwood Brewery initiative, he had not sought to interfere with arrangements already made. However, in the winter of 2003/4, 99 years after its initial introduction, 'Plumage Archer' was once more back on the floors of Warminster's Pound Street maltings.

Chapter 10
THE MALT-STARS SHINE BRIGHT

A thriving business

Toady the Maltings is more than just a thriving business; it has become a bell weather for the emerging UK brewing industry, and is recognised as one of Britain's richest brewing heritage sites.

With close to 250 brewing customers, the sales portfolio now includes a large number of the UK's regional brewers, and many of its original micro-brewery customers have now expanded to the size where their cask ales are achieving wide distribution, and their bottled beers have attained supermarket listing. In the words of the old adage 'what goes round, comes round' we are today witnessing the re-establishment of local breweries all around the country. Garratt would have dismissed all this as his wildest dreams back in 1994.

The Malt-stars, 2009.

But none of this business would have been captured without concerted investment in the refurbishment of the malthouses, new engineering and appropriate new technology in order to optimise production of malt. One notable improvement was to achieve all year round production. At Warminster this has been done with the introduction of chiller radiators on floors 3 and 4.

For ever, 'floor' maltings always ceased production by the end of April or early May as the air temperature began to rise to levels which competed with maltster's ability to manage the floors. In the simplest terms, and in the most extreme cases, despite continuous turning

Wall mounted chiller radiators on floor No. 4.

and all the windows wide open, the 'green' malt would overheat and deteriorate before full 'modification' was achieved. One remedy at Warminster would have been to shut off the floors and install air conditioning. Quite apart from being very expensive, Appel and Garratt felt this was a fundamental change to the natural process, it was also an attack on the architectural integrity of the malthouses, and not only that, for 7–8 months of the year it was unnecessary.

Instead, by mounting chiller radiators into the ceilings of the upper floors, and on the walls of the lower floors, with plastic insulation curtains at each end of each floor, the air temperature above the 'green' malt can now be cooled down in summer to manageable levels without interfering with either the physical or visible access. This investment has proved hugely successful in maintaining summer production and it has been achieved without visibly corrupting the basic layout of Morgan's original malt floors.

Simultaneous with the introduction of new engineering, a lot of time and money was spent on removing the old. This was something that appeared to have been completely overlooked during the last 50 years or so. From day one of his custody Appel had determined to "clear all the crap out of the buildings", and the foreman, Jerry Curtis concurred with this ambition. Seizing every spare moment to mobilize his colleagues into progressing this project, bit by bit Curtis and his men began to make a real difference. Redundant wiring – miles of it; 1950's switchgear – whole walls of it; redundant water pipes, oil tanks of all shapes, size and construction and early conveyors housed in wood casings were all systematically taken apart and cleared from the premises creating a more tidy, cleaner and more manageable working environment. Believe it or not, this task took more than 4 years to complete.

At the same time restoration work continued, albeit one small project at a time. The appointment in 2007 of Mark Young, formerly a maltster, as full-time maintenance officer facilitated this progress. Restoration of each elevation of the malthouses required new doors and new windows, including replacement stone lintels. Cast iron guttering and downpipes collected from reclamation yards were restored and installed where inadequate plastic had been thoughtlessly fitted. To compliment this all the drains had to be cleared and repaired. Then along the north elevation, which had been a depository for the ash from the kilns, as well as a dumping ground for all other rubbish, Appel had the bold idea of creating a small garden.

The design of the window was to prevent maltsters cheating the malt tax by discharging malt through the windows prior to inspection by the Customs and Excise officer.

In the summer of 2001, Appel had been impressed by the cottage gardens immediately adjacent to this piece of ground. They belonged to the next door cottages along Pound Street, and instead of being long narrow strips which ran directly behind each household, the plots had been turned through 90° to create more meaningful spaces serviced by a common footpath which ran along the maltings boundary. Each garden was ornamental rather than allotment, and was a riot of colour all summer long. What is more they were all in regular use, and one Saturday afternoon Appel made a point of apologising for the awful outlook that was the maltings former ash tip. He promised in time he would do something about it.

So in the summer of 2004, work began on a garden. The first job was to lower the ground level to something more akin to its surroundings, so a JCB digger and two tipper lorries were hired to clear the site. Following this, a lawn was laid, borders created, and a hornbeam hedge, the choice of the neighbours, was planted along the boundary. The following spring a small courtyard was created at the western end providing an attractive entrance from the road via the restored gateway from Pound Street.

Today the garden, with its velvet lawn and flourishing borders, provides an attractive venue for entertaining visitors in the summer as well as an additional area of relaxation for the Maltings staff. And, of course, it delivers an outlook for the cottage gardens which at least compliments their own tranquil setting.

"An attractive venue for entertaining visitors in the summer."

Visitors to the Maltings are frequent, both business and pleasure. The latter are entertained with a formal tour of the malthouses, including the laboratory, in order to convey a full understanding of the complexity, and yet the simplicity, of the traditional malting process. The tours normally end with a buffet lunch or supper, washed down with some local ale brewed from Warminster malt, of course, and are proving very popular as word of mouth is spread by those who have been.

But all of the time, Appel and Garratt's principle focus has always been on perfecting production and quality, and building sales. Both men are first and foremost dedicated to the quality of their malt. They recognize that from their own achievements, today's modern band of brewers can go on to deliver lasting success from a proliferation of new beers which are quickly capable of winning national recognition and distribution. A good example would be the Triple FFF brewery in Hampshire. In 2008 the brewery lifted the ultimate brewing trophy when it won the Overall Championship at The Great British Beer Festival at Earl's Court with its ale 'Alton's Pride', brewed with Warminster malt. Sales of this ale sky-rocketed overnight, as every publican in the country sought to include it in its 'guest ale' line up.

Another contribution to this success is that Warminster Maltings occupies a unique spot in the brewery supply chain. First of all, courtesy of Corn Merchants, Robin Appel Ltd, it has a very wide access to barley supplies, and in particular, direct access to the variety 'Maris Otter', production of which is heavily influenced by Appel. Malting barley seed stock and its respective crop husbandry is presided over by the staff of Robin Appel Ltd, which when coupled to the 'hand-made' discipline for malting at Warminster represents a trade mark opportunity akin to "Appellation Contrôlée". Hence a very English "Warranty of Origin" was created in 2006, offering brewers bespoke malt production from barley grown on farms local to the brewery, and the opportunity to put 'Fine Ale' on a parity with 'Fine Wine'! The project was quickly taken up – "Sussex barley for Sussex beer" was one of the first 'Warranty' ales to hit the market, followed by a host of other projects up and down the country.

A new Maltings brochure is launched every year in February, just ahead of the annual SIBA Conference (Society of Independent Brewers) in early March. It portrays a dedication to the quality of their products and a commitment to the success of their customers. Brewers constantly reciprocate with anecdotes which underline the superior quality of Warminster malt. On the back of all this, a new slogan was borne, initially in jest, but it stuck. Today the team that keep Beaven's "old malthouses… still in use" are known far and wide as 'The Malt-stars of Warminster'. It's a title that deserves to be not only bestowed on them, but on all those that for more than 150 years have played their part in maintaining these unique and magical malthouses.

E. S. BEAVEN
POUND STREET. WARMINSTER.

ROADWAY

3700 (G1.3654)

9" walls (23 cms)

121'6

500 to dowls

12

31'10

860 (G1.837)

(G1.807) 22.0

28'3

27'3

120

35-0

KILN

11

(11) door

52.0

21'4

650 (G1.604)

door (11)

14 floor

(22)

170

10

170

120 door

1480

24'6
1 floor

(G1.3410)

13

14·1

13'3 roof

670 (G1.1624)

22.0

10 H

2650 (G1.2604)

950 (G1.944)